Standard Grade | Credit

Mathematics

Leckie×Leckie

First exam published in 2002.
Published by Leckie & Leckie Ltd, 3rd Floor, 4 Queen Street, Edinburgh EH2 1JE
tel: 0131 220 6831 fax: 0131 225 9987 enquiries@leckieandleckie.co.uk www.leckieandleckie.co.uk

ISBN 1-84372-407-3   ISBN-13 978-1-84372-407-0

A CIP Catalogue record for this book is available from the British Library.

Printed in Scotland by Scotprint.

Leckie & Leckie is a division of Granada Learning Limited.

Leckie & Leckie is grateful to the copyright holders, as credited at the back of the book, for permission to use their material.
Every effort has been made to trace the copyright holders and to obtain their permission for the use of copyright material.
Leckie & Leckie will gladly receive information enabling them to rectify any error or omission in subsequent editions.

2002 | Credit

[BLANK PAGE]

C

2500/405

NATIONAL QUALIFICATIONS 2002	THURSDAY, 9 MAY 1.30 PM – 2.25 PM	**MATHEMATICS** STANDARD GRADE Credit Level Paper 1 (Non-calculator)

1 **You may NOT use a calculator**.

2 Answer as many questions as you can.

3 Full credit will be given only where the solution contains appropriate working.

4 Square-ruled paper is provided.

SCOTTISH
QUALIFICATIONS
AUTHORITY

©

FORMULAE LIST

The roots of $ax^2 + bx + c = 0$ are $x = \dfrac{-b \pm \sqrt{(b^2 - 4ac)}}{2a}$

Sine rule: $\dfrac{a}{\sin A} = \dfrac{b}{\sin B} = \dfrac{c}{\sin C}$

Cosine rule: $a^2 = b^2 + c^2 - 2bc\cos A$ or $\cos A = \dfrac{b^2 + c^2 - a^2}{2bc}$

Area of a triangle: $\text{Area} = \tfrac{1}{2}ab\sin C$

Standard deviation: $s = \sqrt{\dfrac{\sum(x - \bar{x})^2}{n-1}} = \sqrt{\dfrac{\sum x^2 - (\sum x)^2/n}{n-1}}$, where n is the sample size.

KU | RE

1. Evaluate
$$7 \cdot 18 - 2 \cdot 1 \times 3.$$

2. Evaluate
$$1\tfrac{1}{8} \div \tfrac{3}{4}.$$

3. Solve the inequality $5 - x > 2(x + 1)$.

4. Given that $f(x) = x^2 + 5x$, evaluate $f(-3)$.

5. (a) Factorise $p^2 - 4q^2$.

   (b) Hence simplify
   $$\frac{p^2 - 4q^2}{3p + 6q}.$$

6. $L = \tfrac{1}{2}(h - t)$.

   Change the subject of the formula to h.

[Turn over

KU | RE

7. In triangle ABC,

AB = 4 units
AC = 5 units
BC = 6 units.

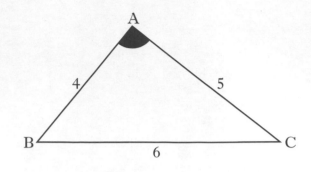

Show that $\cos A = \frac{1}{8}$.

3

8. Fifteen medical centres each **handed out** a questionnaire to fifty patients.

The numbers who replied to each centre are shown below.

11	19	22	25	25
29	31	34	36	38
40	46	49	50	50

Also, they each **posted** the questionnaire to another fifty patients.

The numbers who replied to each centre are shown below.

15	15	21	22	23
25	26	31	33	34
37	39	41	46	46

Draw an appropriate statistical diagram to compare these two sets of data.

3

9. Two functions are given below.

$$f(x) = x^2 + 2x - 1$$
$$g(x) = 5x + 3$$

Find the values of x for which $f(x) = g(x)$.

3

KU | RE

10. Simplify

$$\sqrt{27} + 2\sqrt{3}.$$

2

11. Express in its simplest form

$$y^8 \times (y^3)^{-2}.$$

2

12. The graph below shows the relationship between the history and geography marks of a class of students.

A best-fitting straight line, AB has been drawn.

Point A represents 0 marks for history and 12 marks for geography.
Point B represents 90 marks for history and 82 marks for geography.

Find the equation of the straight line AB in terms of *h* and *g*.

4

[Turn over for Question 13 on *Page six*

KU | RE

13. (*a*) 4 peaches and 3 grapefruit cost £1·30.

Write down an algebraic equation to illustrate this.

1

(*b*) 2 peaches and 4 grapefruit cost £1·20.

Write down an algebraic equation to illustrate this.

1

(*c*) Find the cost of 3 peaches and 2 grapefruit.

4

[END OF QUESTION PAPER]

C

2500/406

NATIONAL
QUALIFICATIONS
2002

THURSDAY, 9 MAY
2.45 PM – 4.05 PM

MATHEMATICS
STANDARD GRADE
Credit Level
Paper 2

1 **You may use a calculator**.

2 Answer as many questions as you can.

3 Full credit will be given only where the solution contains appropriate working.

4 Square-ruled paper is provided.

SCOTTISH
QUALIFICATIONS
AUTHORITY

FORMULAE LIST

The roots of $ax^2 + bx + c = 0$ are $x = \dfrac{-b \pm \sqrt{(b^2 - 4ac)}}{2a}$

Sine rule: $\dfrac{a}{\sin A} = \dfrac{b}{\sin B} = \dfrac{c}{\sin C}$

Cosine rule: $a^2 = b^2 + c^2 - 2bc \cos A$ or $\cos A = \dfrac{b^2 + c^2 - a^2}{2bc}$

Area of a triangle: $\text{Area} = \frac{1}{2}ab \sin C$

Standard deviation: $s = \sqrt{\dfrac{\sum(x - \bar{x})^2}{n-1}} = \sqrt{\dfrac{\sum x^2 - (\sum x)^2 / n}{n-1}}$, where n is the sample size.

	KU	RE

1. A spider weighs approximately $19{\cdot}06 \times 10^{-5}$ kilograms.

A humming bird is 18 times heavier.

Calculate the weight of the humming bird.

Give your answer **in scientific notation**.

2

2. A microwave oven is sold for £150.

This price includes VAT at 17·5%.

Calculate the price of the microwave oven **without** VAT.

3

3. Solve the equation

$$2x^2 + 3x - 7 = 0.$$

Give your answers **correct to 1 decimal place**.

4

[Turn over

KU | RE

4. A TV signal is sent from a transmitter T, via a satellite S, to a village V, as shown in the diagram. The village is 500 kilometres from the transmitter.

The signal is sent out at an angle of 35° and is received in the village at an angle of 40°.

Calculate the height of the satellite above the ground.

5

5. A feeding trough, 4 metres long, is prism-shaped.

The uniform cross-section is made up of a rectangle and semi-circle as shown below.

 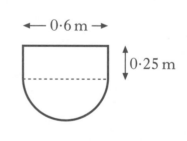

Find the volume of the trough, **correct to 2 significant figures**.

5

KU | RE

6. An oil tank has a circular cross-section of radius 2·1 metres.

It is filled to a depth of 3·4 metres.

 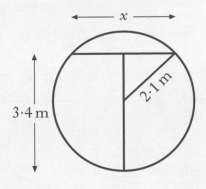

(a) Calculate x, the width in metres of the oil surface.   3

(b) What other depth of oil would give the same surface width?   1

7. A coffee shop blends its own coffee and sells it in one-kilogram tins.

One blend consists of two kinds of coffee, Brazilian and Colombian, in the ratio 2 : 3.

The shop has 20 kilograms of Brazilian and 25 kilograms of Colombian in stock.

What is the **maximum** number of one-kilogram tins of this blend which can be made?   3

[Turn over

KU | RE

8. The diagram shows part of the graph of $y = \sin x°$.

The line $y = 0·4$ is drawn and cuts the graph of $y = \sin x°$ at A and B.

Find the x-coordinates of A and B.

3

9. Esther has a new mobile phone and considers the following daily rates.

Easy Call	**Green Call**
25 pence per minute for the first 3 minutes	40 pence per minute for the first 2 minutes
5 pence per minute **after** the first three minutes	2 pence per minute **after** the first two minutes

(a) For Easy Call, find the cost of ten minutes in a day.

1

(b) For Easy Call, find a formula for the cost of "m" minutes in a day, $m > 3$.

1

(c) For Green Call, find a formula for the cost of "m" minutes in a day, $m > 2$.

1

(d) Green Call claims that its system is cheaper.

Find **algebraically** the least number of minutes (to the nearest minute) which must be used each day for this claim to be true.

3

KU | RE

10. A weight on the end of a string is spun in a circle on a smooth table.

The tension, T, in the string varies directly as the square of the speed, v, and inversely as the radius, r, of the circle.

(a) Write down a formula for T in terms of v and r.

1

(b) The speed of the weight is multiplied by 3 and the radius of the string is halved.

What happens to the tension in the string?

2

11. (a) Solve the equation

$$2^n = 32.$$

1

(b) A sequence of numbers can be grouped and added together as shown.

The sum of 2 numbers: $(1 + 2) = 4 - 1$
The sum of 3 numbers: $(1 + 2 + 4) = 8 - 1$
The sum of 4 numbers: $(1 + 2 + 4 + 8) = 16 - 1$

Find a **similar** expression for the sum of 5 numbers.

1

(c) Find a formula for the sum of the first n numbers of this sequence.

2

[Turn over for Question 12 on *Page eight*

KU RE

12. A metal beam, AB, is 6 metres long.

It is hinged at the top, P, of a vertical post 1 metre high.

When B touches the ground, A is 1·5 metres above the ground, as shown in Figure 1.

Figure 1

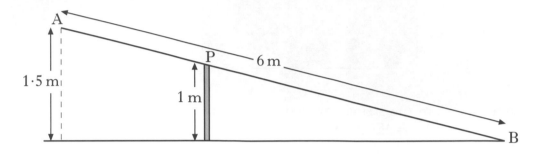

When A comes down to the ground, B rises, as shown in Figure 2.

Figure 2

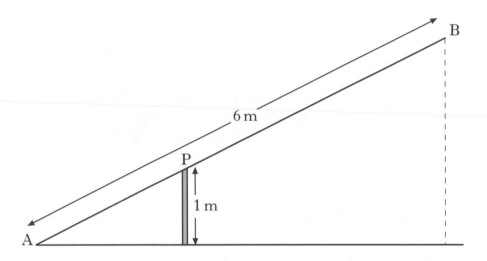

By calculating the length of AP, or otherwise, find the height of B above the ground.

Do not use a scale drawing.

5

[END OF QUESTION PAPER]

[BLANK PAGE]

C

2500/405

| NATIONAL QUALIFICATIONS 2003 | THURSDAY, 8 MAY 1.30 PM – 2.25 PM | MATHEMATICS STANDARD GRADE Credit Level Paper 1 (Non-calculator) |

1 **You may NOT use a calculator**.

2 Answer as many questions as you can.

3 Full credit will be given only where the solution contains appropriate working.

4 Square-ruled paper is provided.

SCOTTISH QUALIFICATIONS AUTHORITY

©

FORMULAE LIST

The roots of $ax^2 + bx + c = 0$ are $x = \dfrac{-b \pm \sqrt{(b^2 - 4ac)}}{2a}$

Sine rule: $\dfrac{a}{\sin A} = \dfrac{b}{\sin B} = \dfrac{c}{\sin C}$

Cosine rule: $a^2 = b^2 + c^2 - 2bc \cos A$ or $\cos A = \dfrac{b^2 + c^2 - a^2}{2bc}$

Area of a triangle: $\text{Area} = \tfrac{1}{2} ab \sin C$

Standard deviation: $s = \sqrt{\dfrac{\sum (x - \bar{x})^2}{n-1}} = \sqrt{\dfrac{\sum x^2 - (\sum x)^2 / n}{n-1}}$, where n is the sample size.

		KU	RE

1. Evaluate $\qquad$ $5{\cdot}04 + 8{\cdot}4 \div 7.$ $\qquad$ 2

2. Evaluate $\qquad$ $\frac{2}{7}(1\frac{3}{4} + \frac{3}{8}).$ $\qquad$ 2

3. Simplify $\qquad$ $3(2x - 4) - 4(3x + 1).$ $\qquad$ 3

4. $\qquad\qquad$ $f(x) - 7 - 4x$

    (*a*) Evaluate $f(-2).$ $\qquad$ 1

    (*b*) Given that $f(t) = 9$, find t. $\qquad$ 2

5. Factorise
$\qquad\qquad$ $2x^2 - 7x - 15.$ $\qquad$ 2

[Turn over

KU | RE

6. In the diagram below, A is the point $(-1, -7)$ and B is the point $(4, 3)$.

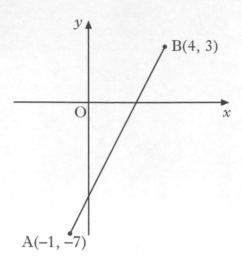

(a) Find the gradient of the line AB.

1

(b) AB cuts the y-axis at the point $(0, -5)$.

Write down the equation of the line AB.

1

(c) The point $(3k, k)$ lies on AB.

Find the value of k.

2

7. Andrew and Doreen each book in at the Sleepwell Lodge.

(a) Andrew stays for 3 nights and has breakfast on 2 mornings.

His bill is £145.

Write down an algebraic equation to illustrate this.

1

(b) Doreen stays for 5 nights and has breakfast on 3 mornings.

Her bill is £240.

Write down an algebraic equation to illustrate this.

1

(c) Find the cost of one breakfast.

3

KU | RE

8. A mini lottery game uses **red**, **green**, **blue** and **yellow** balls.

There are 10 of **each** colour, numbered from 1 to 10.

The balls are placed in a drum and one is drawn out.

(a) What is the probability that it is a **6**?   1

(b) What is the probability that it is a **yellow 6**?   1

9. A random check is carried out on the contents of a number of matchboxes.

A summary of the results is shown in the boxplot below.

47   50   51   53   54

What percentage of matchboxes contains fewer than 50 matches?   1

10. School theatre visits are arranged for parents, teachers and pupils.

The ratio of parents to teachers to pupils **must** be 1 : 3 : 15.

(a) 45 pupils want to go to the theatre.

How many teachers must accompany them?   1

(b) The theatre gives the school 100 tickets for a play.

What is the maximum number of pupils who can go to the play?   3

[Turn over

KU | RE

11. Using the sequence

$$1, \quad 3, \quad 5, \quad 7, \quad 9, \ldots.$$

(a) Find S_3, the sum of the first 3 numbers.

         1

(b) Find S_n, the sum of the first n numbers.

         2

(c) Hence or otherwise, find the $(n + 1)^{\text{th}}$ term of the sequence.

         2

12. (a) Evaluate

$$8^{\frac{2}{3}}.$$

   2

(b) Simplify

$$\frac{\sqrt{24}}{\sqrt{2}}.$$

   2

13. A rectangular clipboard has a triangular plastic pocket attached as shown in Figure 1.

Figure 1

The pocket is attached along edges TD and DB as shown in Figure 2.

B is x centimetres from the corner C.

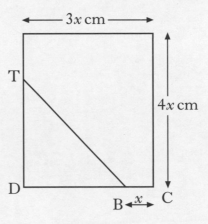

Figure 2

The length of the clipboard is $4x$ centimetres and the breadth is $3x$ centimetres.

The area of the pocket is a quarter of the area of the clipboard.

Find, in terms of x, the length of TD.

4

[END OF QUESTION PAPER]

[BLANK PAGE]

C

2500/406

NATIONAL
QUALIFICATIONS
2003

THURSDAY, 8 MAY
2.45 PM – 4.05 PM

MATHEMATICS
STANDARD GRADE
Credit Level
Paper 2

1 **You may use a calculator.**

2 Answer as many questions as you can.

3 Full credit will be given only where the solution contains appropriate working.

4 Square-ruled paper is provided.

SCOTTISH
QUALIFICATIONS
AUTHORITY

©

FORMULAE LIST

The roots of $ax^2 + bx + c = 0$ are $x = \dfrac{-b \pm \sqrt{(b^2 - 4ac)}}{2a}$

Sine rule: $\dfrac{a}{\sin A} = \dfrac{b}{\sin B} = \dfrac{c}{\sin C}$

Cosine rule: $a^2 = b^2 + c^2 - 2bc \cos A$ or $\cos A = \dfrac{b^2 + c^2 - a^2}{2bc}$

Area of a triangle: Area $= \frac{1}{2} ab \sin C$

Standard deviation: $s = \sqrt{\dfrac{\sum (x - \bar{x})^2}{n-1}} = \sqrt{\dfrac{\sum x^2 - (\sum x)^2 / n}{n-1}}$, where n is the sample size.

KU | RE

1. Bacteria in a test-tube increase at the rate of 0·6% per hour.

   At 12 noon, there are 5000 bacteria.

   At 3pm, how many bacteria will be present?

   Give your answer **to 3 significant figures**.

   4

2. Fiona checks out the price of a litre of milk in several shops.

   The prices in pence are:

   $$49 \quad 44 \quad 41 \quad 52 \quad 47 \quad 43.$$

   (a) Find the mean price of a litre of milk.

   1

   (b) Find the standard deviation of the prices.

   2

   (c) Fiona also checks out the price of a kilogram of sugar in the same shops and finds that the standard deviation of the prices is 2·6.

   Make one valid comparison between the two sets of prices.

   1

3. Two yachts leave from harbour H.

   Yacht A sails on a bearing of 072° for 30 kilometres and stops.

   Yacht B sails on a bearing of 140° for 50 kilometres and stops.

   How far apart are the two yachts when they have both stopped?

   Do not use a scale drawing.

   4

[Turn over

4. A mug is in the shape of a cylinder with diameter 10 centimetres and height 14 centimetres.

(a) Calculate the volume of the mug.

(b) 600 millilitres of coffee are poured in.

Calculate the depth of the coffee in the cup.

5. The number of diagonals, d, in a polygon with n sides is given by the formula

$$d = \frac{n(n-3)}{2}.$$

A polygon has 20 diagonals.

How many sides does it have?

6. In the diagram,

Angle STV = 34°

Angle VSW = 25°

Angle SVT = Angle SWV = 90°

ST = 13·1 centimetres.

Calculate the length of SW.

KU | RE

7. The area of triangle ABC is 38 square centimetres.

AB is 9 centimetres and BC is 14 centimetres.

Calculate the size of the acute angle ABC.

3

8. The diagram below shows part of the graph of a quadratic function, with equation of the form $y = k(x - a)(x - b)$.

The graph cuts the y-axis at $(0, -6)$ and the x-axis at $(-1, 0)$ and $(3, 0)$.

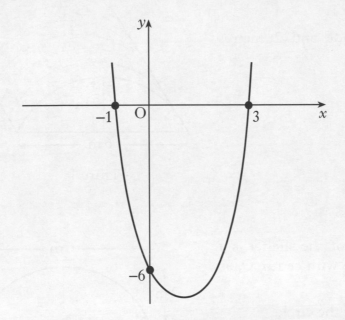

(a) Write down the values of a and b.

2

(b) Calculate the value of k.

2

(c) Find the coordinates of the minimum turning point of the function.

2

[Turn over

9. Two perfume bottles are mathematically similar in shape.

The smaller one is 6 centimetres high and holds 30 millilitres of perfume.

The larger one is 9 centimetres high.

What volume of perfume will the larger one hold?

3

10. A sheep shelter is part of a cylinder as shown in Figure 1.

It is 6 metres wide and 2 metres high.

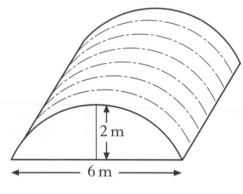

Figure 1

The cross-section of the shelter is a segment of a circle with centre O, as shown in Figure 2.

OB is the radius of the circle.

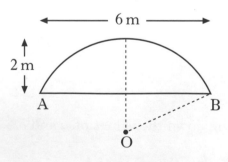

Figure 2

Calculate the length of OB.

4

	KU	RE

11. (*a*) A driver travels from A to B, a distance of *x* kilometres, at a constant speed of 75 kilometres per hour.

Find the time taken for this journey in terms of *x*.

(*b*) The time for the journey from B to A is $\frac{x}{50}$ hours.

Hence calculate the driver's average speed for the whole journey.

1

4

[END OF QUESTION PAPER]

[BLANK PAGE]

2004 | Credit

[BLANK PAGE]

C

2500/405

NATIONAL
QUALIFICATIONS
2004

FRIDAY, 7 MAY
1.30 PM – 2.25 PM

MATHEMATICS
STANDARD GRADE
Credit Level
Paper 1
(Non-calculator)

1 **You may NOT use a calculator**.

2 Answer as many questions as you can.

3 Full credit will be given only where the solution contains appropriate working.

4 Square-ruled paper is provided.

SCOTTISH
QUALIFICATIONS
AUTHORITY

FORMULAE LIST

The roots of $ax^2 + bx + c = 0$ are $x = \dfrac{-b \pm \sqrt{(b^2 - 4ac)}}{2a}$

Sine rule: $\dfrac{a}{\sin A} = \dfrac{b}{\sin B} = \dfrac{c}{\sin C}$

Cosine rule: $a^2 = b^2 + c^2 - 2bc \cos A$ or $\cos A = \dfrac{b^2 + c^2 - a^2}{2bc}$

Area of a triangle: $\text{Area} = \frac{1}{2} ab \sin C$

Standard deviation: $s = \sqrt{\dfrac{\sum (x - \bar{x})^2}{n-1}} = \sqrt{\dfrac{\sum x^2 - (\sum x)^2 / n}{n-1}}$, where n is the sample size.

	KU	RE

1. Evaluate

$$6\cdot2 - (4\cdot53 - 1\cdot1).$$

   KU **2**

2. Evaluate $\qquad \frac{2}{5}$ of $3\frac{1}{2} + \frac{4}{5}$

   KU **3**

3. $A = 2x^2 - y^2$.

   Calculate the value of A when $x = 3$ and $y = -4$.

   KU **2**

4. Simplify $\qquad \dfrac{3}{m} + \dfrac{4}{(m+1)}$

   KU **3**

5. The average monthly temperature in a holiday resort was recorded in degrees Celsius (°C).

Month	Jan	Feb	Mar	Apr	May	June	July	Aug	Sept	Oct	Nov	Dec
Average Temperature (°C)	1	8	8	10	15	22	23	24	20	14	9	4

   Draw a suitable statistical diagram to illustrate the median and the quartiles of this data.

   RE **4**

[Turn over

KU | RE

6. Marmalade is on special offer.

Each jar on special offer contains 12·5% more than the standard jar.

A jar on special offer contains 450 g of marmalade.

How much does the standard jar contain?

3

7. John's school sells 1200 tickets for a raffle.

John buys 15 tickets.

John's church sells 1800 tickets for a raffle.

John buys 20 tickets.

In which raffle has he a better chance of winning the first prize?

Show clearly all your working.

3

KU | RE

8.   7,   −2,   5,   3,   8

In the sequence above, each term after the first two terms is the sum of the previous two terms.

For example: 3rd term = 5 = 7 + (−2)

(a)   A sequence follows the above rule.

The first term is x and the second term is y.

The fifth term is 5.

x, y,   −,   −,   5

Show that $2x + 3y = 5$

2

(b)   Using the same x and y, another sequence follows the above rule.

The first term is y and the second term is x.

The sixth term is 17.

y, x,   −,   −,   −,   17.

Write down another equation in x and y.

2

(c)   Find the values of x and y.

3

9.   The graph of $y = a \cos bx°$, $0 \leq x \leq 90$, is shown below.

Write down the values of a and b.

2

[Turn over for Questions 10, 11 and 12 on *Page six*

KU | RE

10. Two variables x and y are connected by the relationship $y = ax + b$.

Sketch a possible graph of y against x to illustrate this relationship when a and b are each less than zero.

3

11. (*a*) Simplify $\quad 2\sqrt{75}$

2

    (*b*) Evaluate $\quad 2^0 + 3^{-1}$.

2

12. A piece of gold wire 10 centimetres long is made into a circle.

10 cm

The circumference of the circle is equal to the length of the wire.

Show that the area of the circle is **exactly** $\dfrac{25}{\pi}$ square centimetres.

4

[END OF QUESTION PAPER]

C

2500/406

NATIONAL
QUALIFICATIONS
2004

FRIDAY, 7 MAY
2.45 PM – 4.05 PM

MATHEMATICS
STANDARD GRADE
Credit Level
Paper 2

1 **You may use a calculator**.

2 Answer as many questions as you can.

3 Full credit will be given only where the solution contains appropriate working.

4 Square-ruled paper is provided.

FORMULAE LIST

The roots of $ax^2 + bx + c = 0$ are $x = \dfrac{-b \pm \sqrt{(b^2 - 4ac)}}{2a}$

Sine rule: $\dfrac{a}{\sin A} = \dfrac{b}{\sin B} = \dfrac{c}{\sin C}$

Cosine rule: $a^2 = b^2 + c^2 - 2bc\,\cos A$ or $\cos A = \dfrac{b^2 + c^2 - a^2}{2bc}$

Area of a triangle: Area $= \frac{1}{2}ab\sin C$

Standard deviation: $s = \sqrt{\dfrac{\sum(x - \bar{x})^2}{n - 1}} = \sqrt{\dfrac{\sum x^2 - (\sum x)^2 / n}{n - 1}}$, where n is the sample size.

KU | RE

1. Radio signals travel at a speed of 3×10^8 metres per second.

   A radio signal from Earth to a space probe takes 8 hours.

   What is the distance from Earth to the probe?

   Give your answer **in scientific notation**.

   KU **4**

2. A tank which holds 100 litres of water has a leak.

   After 150 minutes, there is no water left in the tank.

   The above graph represents the volume of water (v litres) against time (t minutes).

   (a) Find the equation of the line in terms of v and t.

   KU **3**

   (b) How many minutes does it take for the container to lose 30 litres of water?

   RE **3**

3. Bottles of juice should contain 50 millilitres.

   The contents of 7 bottles are checked in a random sample.

   The actual volumes in millilitres are as shown below.

   $$52, \quad 50, \quad 51, \quad 49, \quad 52, \quad 53, \quad 50$$

   Calculate the mean and standard deviation of the sample.

   KU **4**

KU | RE

4. 250 milligrams of a drug are given to a patient at 12 noon.

The amount of the drug in the bloodstream decreases by 20% every hour.

How many milligrams of the drug are in the bloodstream at 3pm?

3

5. A helicopter, at point H, hovers between two aircraft carriers at points A and B which are 1500 metres apart.

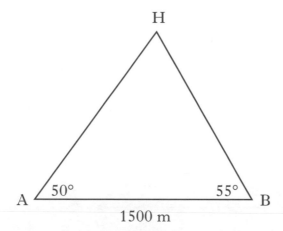

From carrier A, the angle of elevation of the helicopter is 50°.

From carrier B, the angle of elevation of the helicopter is 55°.

Calculate the distance from the helicopter to the nearer carrier.

4

KU | RE

6. The diagram below shows a spotlight at point S, mounted 10 metres directly above a point P at the front edge of a stage.

The spotlight swings 45° from the vertical to illuminate another point Q, also at the front edge of the stage.

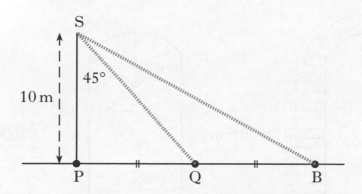

Through how many **more** degrees must the spotlight swing to illuminate a point B, where Q is the mid-point of PB?

5

7. A square trapdoor of side 80 centimetres is held open by a rod as shown.

The rod is attached to a corner of the trapdoor and placed 40 centimetres along the edge of the opening.

The angle between the trapdoor and the opening is 76°.

Calculate the length of the rod to **2 significant figures**.

4

[Turn over

8. The curved part of a doorway is an arc of a circle with radius 500 millimetres and centre C.

   The height of the doorway to the top of the arc is 2000 millimetres.

   The vertical edge of the doorway is 1800 millimetres.

   Calculate the width of the doorway.

   5

9. A gift box, 8 centimetres high, is prism shaped.

   The uniform cross-section is a regular pentagon.

   Each vertex of the pentagon is 10 centimetres from the centre O.

   Calculate the volume of the box.

   5

KU | RE

10. Solve **algebraically** the equation

$$4 \sin x° + 1 = -2 \qquad 0 \leq x < 360.$$

3

11. A rectangular lawn has a path, 1 metre wide, on 3 sides as shown.

The breadth of the lawn is x metres.

The length of the lawn is three times its breadth.

The area of the lawn equals the area of the path.

(a) Show that $3x^2 - 5x - 2 = 0$.

3

(b) Hence find the **length** of the lawn.

4

[END OF QUESTION PAPER]

[BLANK PAGE]

2005 | Credit

[BLANK PAGE]

C

2500/405

NATIONAL
QUALIFICATIONS
2005

FRIDAY, 6 MAY
1.30 PM – 2.25 PM

MATHEMATICS
STANDARD GRADE
Credit Level
Paper 1
(Non-calculator)

1 **You may NOT use a calculator**.

2 Answer as many questions as you can.

3 Full credit will be given only where the solution contains appropriate working.

4 Square-ruled paper is provided.

SCOTTISH
QUALIFICATIONS
AUTHORITY

©

FORMULAE LIST

The roots of $ax^2 + bx + c = 0$ are $x = \dfrac{-b \pm \sqrt{(b^2 - 4ac)}}{2a}$

Sine rule: $\dfrac{a}{\sin A} = \dfrac{b}{\sin B} = \dfrac{c}{\sin C}$

Cosine rule: $a^2 = b^2 + c^2 - 2bc\,\cos A$ or $\cos A = \dfrac{b^2 + c^2 - a^2}{2bc}$

Area of a triangle: Area $= \frac{1}{2}ab\sin C$

Standard deviation: $s = \sqrt{\dfrac{\sum(x - \bar{x})^2}{n-1}} = \sqrt{\dfrac{\sum x^2 - (\sum x)^2 / n}{n-1}}$, where n is the sample size.

KU | RE

1. Evaluate

$$3\cdot8 - (7\cdot36 \div 8).$$

2

2. Evaluate

$$2\tfrac{1}{3} + \tfrac{5}{6} \text{ of } 1\tfrac{2}{5}.$$

3

3. Evaluate

$$12\cdot5\% \text{ of } £140.$$

2

4. Two identical dice are rolled simultaneously.

Find the probability that the total score on adding both numbers will be greater than 7 but less than 10.

2

[Turn over

	KU	RE

5. In an experiment involving two variables, the following values for x and y were recorded.

x	0	1	2	3	4
y	6	4	2	0	-2

The results were plotted, and a straight line was drawn through the points. Find the gradient of the line **and** write down its equation.

3

6. Solve the equation

$$\frac{2}{x}+1=6.$$

3

7. The speeds (measured to the nearest 10 kilometres per hour) of 200 vehicles are recorded as shown.

$Speed$ (km/hr)	30	40	50	60	70	80	90	100	110
$Frequency$	1	4	9	14	38	47	51	32	4

Construct a cumulative frequency table and hence find the median for this data.

3

8. A number pattern is given below.

1st term: $2^2 - 0^2$
2nd term: $3^2 - 1^2$
3rd term: $4^2 - 2^2$

(a) Write down a similar expression for the 4th term.

1

(b) Hence or otherwise find the nth term in its simplest form.

3

| | KU | RE |

9. (a) Emma puts £30 worth of petrol into the empty fuel tank of her car.

Petrol costs 75 pence per litre.
Her car uses 5 litres of petrol per hour, when she drives at a particular constant speed.

At this constant speed, how many litres of petrol will remain in the car after 3 hours?

2

(b) The next week, Emma puts £20 worth of petrol into the empty fuel tank of her car.

Petrol costs c pence per litre.
Her car uses k litres of petrol per hour, when she drives at another constant speed.

Find a formula for R, the amount of petrol remaining in the car after t hours.

3

10. A badge is made from a circle of radius 5 centimetres.

Segments are taken off the top and the bottom of the circle as shown.

The straight edges are parallel.

The badge measures 7 centimetres from the top to the bottom.
The top is 8 centimetres wide.

Calculate the width of the base.

5

[Turn over

KU RE

11. $f(x) = 4\sqrt{x} + \sqrt{2}$

(a) Find the value of $f(72)$ as a surd in its simplest form.   3

(b) Find the value of t, given that $f(t) = 3\sqrt{2}$.   3

12. The height of a triangle is $(2x - 5)$ centimetres and the base is $2x$ centimetres.

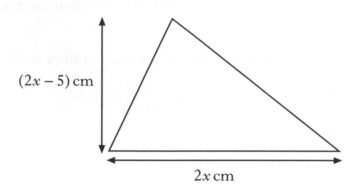

$(2x - 5)$ cm

$2x$ cm

The area of the triangle is 7 square centimetres.

Calculate the value of x.   5

[END OF QUESTION PAPER]

C

2500/406

NATIONAL
QUALIFICATIONS
2005

FRIDAY, 6 MAY
2.45 PM – 4.05 PM

MATHEMATICS
STANDARD GRADE
Credit Level
Paper 2

1 **You may use a calculator**.

2 Answer as many questions as you can.

3 Full credit will be given only where the solution contains appropriate working.

4 Square-ruled paper is provided.

SCOTTISH
QUALIFICATIONS
AUTHORITY

©

FORMULAE LIST

The roots of $ax^2 + bx + c = 0$ are $x = \dfrac{-b \pm \sqrt{(b^2 - 4ac)}}{2a}$

Sine rule: $\dfrac{a}{\sin A} = \dfrac{b}{\sin B} = \dfrac{c}{\sin C}$

Cosine rule: $a^2 = b^2 + c^2 - 2bc \cos A$ or $\cos A = \dfrac{b^2 + c^2 - a^2}{2bc}$

Area of a triangle: Area $= \tfrac{1}{2} ab \sin C$

Standard deviation: $s = \sqrt{\dfrac{\sum(x - \bar{x})^2}{n-1}} = \sqrt{\dfrac{\sum x^2 - (\sum x)^2 / n}{n-1}}$, where n is the sample size.

KU | RE

1. $$E = mc^2.$$

Find the value of E when $m = 3 \cdot 6 \times 10^{-2}$ and $c = 3 \times 10^8$.

Give your answer **in scientific notation**.

3

2.   The running times in minutes, of 6 television programmes are:

    77   91   84   71   79   75.

Calculate the mean and standard deviation of these times.

4

3.

Calculate the area of triangle PQR.

4

4.   Solve the equation

    $$x^2 + 2x = 9.$$

Give your answers **correct to 1 decimal place**.

3

[Turn over

5. A triangular paving slab has measurements as shown.

Is the slab in the shape of a right-angled triangle?

Show your working.

3

6. A vertical flagpole 12 metres high stands at the centre of the roof of a tower.

The tower is cuboid shaped with a square base of side 10 metres.

At a point P on the ground, 20 metres from the base of the tower, the top of the flagpole is just visible, as shown.

Calculate the height of the tower.

4

	KU	RE

7. David walks on a bearing of 050° from hostel A to a viewpoint V, 5 kilometres away.

Hostel B is due east of hostel A.

Susie walks on a bearing of 294° from hostel B to the same viewpoint.

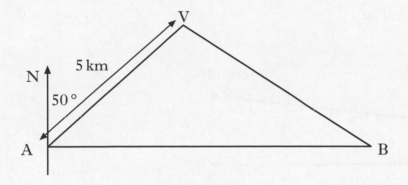

Calculate the length of AB, the distance between the two hostels. | | 5

8. The side length of a cube is $2x$ centimetres.

←—$2x$ cm—→

The expression for the volume in cubic centimetres is equal to the expression for the surface area in square centimetres.

Calculate the side length of the cube. | | 5

[Turn over

KU | RE

9. The monthly bill for a mobile phone is made up of a fixed rental plus call charges. Call charges vary as the time used.

    The relationship between the monthly bill, y (pounds), and the time used, x (minutes) is represented in the graph below.

    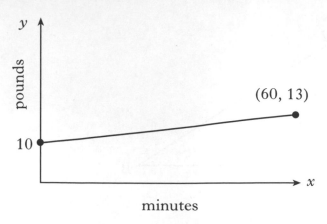

    (a) Write down the fixed rental.   **1**

    (b) Find the call charge per minute.   **3**

10. The chain of a demolition ball is 12·5 metres long.

    When vertical, the end of the chain is 1·5 metres from the ground.

    It swings to a maximum height of 2·5 metres above the ground on both sides.

    (a) At this maximum height, show that the angle $x°$, which the chain makes with the vertical, is approximately 23°.   **4**

    (b) Calculate the maximum length of the arc through which the end of the chain swings. Give your answer **to 3 significant figures**.   **4**

KU RE

11. (*a*) Solve algebraically the equation

$$\sqrt{3}\sin x° - 1 = 0 \qquad 0 \le x < 360.$$

3

(*b*) Hence write down the solution of the equation

$$\sqrt{3}\sin 2x° - 1 = 0 \qquad 0 \le x < 90.$$

1

[*END OF QUESTION PAPER*]

[BLANK PAGE]

[BLANK PAGE]

C

2500/405

NATIONAL
QUALIFICATIONS
2006

FRIDAY, 5 MAY
1.30 PM – 2.25 PM

MATHEMATICS
STANDARD GRADE
Credit Level
Paper 1
(Non-calculator)

1 **You may NOT use a calculator.**

2 Answer as many questions as you can.

3 Full credit will be given only where the solution contains appropriate working.

4 Square-ruled paper is provided.

SCOTTISH
QUALIFICATIONS
AUTHORITY

FORMULAE LIST

The roots of $ax^2 + bx + c = 0$ are $x = \dfrac{-b \pm \sqrt{(b^2 - 4ac)}}{2a}$

Sine rule: $\dfrac{a}{\sin A} = \dfrac{b}{\sin B} = \dfrac{c}{\sin C}$

Cosine rule: $a^2 = b^2 + c^2 - 2bc \cos A$ or $\cos A = \dfrac{b^2 + c^2 - a^2}{2bc}$

Area of a triangle: Area $= \frac{1}{2}ab \sin C$

Standard deviation: $s = \sqrt{\dfrac{\sum(x - \bar{x})^2}{n - 1}} = \sqrt{\dfrac{\sum x^2 - (\sum x)^2 / n}{n - 1}}$, where n is the sample size.

KU | RE

1. Evaluate

$$56{\cdot}4 - 1{\cdot}25 \times 40.$$

2

2. Evaluate

$$1\tfrac{3}{5} + 2\tfrac{4}{7}.$$

2

3. Given that $f(x) = 4 - x^2$, evaluate $f(-3)$.

2

4.

Find the equation of the given straight line.

3

[Turn over

KU | RE

5. (a) Factorise

$$4x^2 - y^2.$$

1

(b) Hence simplify

$$\frac{4x^2 - y^2}{6x + 3y}.$$

2

6. Solve the equation

$$x - 2(x + 1) = 8.$$

3

7. Coffee is sold in regular cups and large cups.

The two cups are mathematically similar in shape.

Regular   Large

The regular cup is 14 centimetres high and holds 160 millilitres.

The large cup is 21 centimetres high.

Calculate how many millilitres the large cup holds.

4

8. The graph of $y = x^2$ has been moved to the position shown in Figure 1.

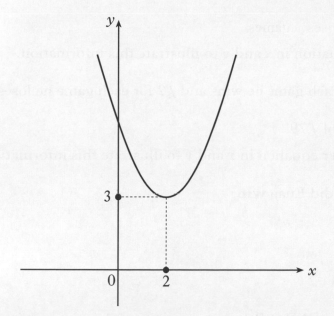

Figure 1

The equation of this graph is $y = (x-2)^2 + 3$.

The graph of $y = x^2$ has now been moved to the position shown in Figure 2.

Figure 2

Write down the equation of the graph in Figure 2.

[Turn over

KU | RE

9. Euan plays in a snooker tournament which consists of 20 games.

He wins x games and loses y games.

(a) Write down an equation in x and y to illustrate this information.

1

(b) He is paid £5 for each game he wins and £2 for each game he loses.

He is paid a **total** of £79.

Write down another equation in x and y to illustrate this information.

2

(c) How many games did Euan **win**?

3

10. Triangle ABC is right-angled at B.

The dimensions are as shown.

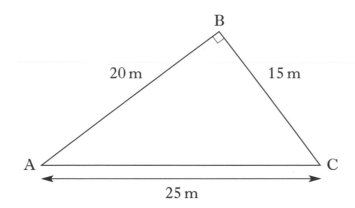

(a) Calculate the area of triangle ABC.

1

(b) BD, the height of triangle ABC, is drawn as shown.

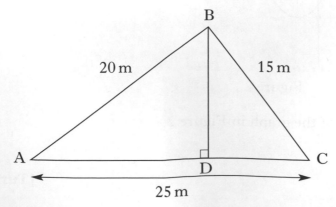

Use your answer to part (a) to calculate the height BD.

3

	KU	RE

11. (a) One session at the Leisure Centre costs £3.

£3 per session

Write down an algebraic expression for the cost of x sessions.   **1**

(b) The Leisure Centre also offers a monthly card costing £20. The **first 6** sessions are then free, with each additional session costing £2.

Monthly card
£20

* first 6 sessions **free**
* each additional
  session £2

   (i) Find the **total** cost of a monthly card and 15 sessions.   **1**

   (ii) Write down an algebraic expression for the **total** cost of a monthly card and x **sessions**, where x is greater than 6.   **2**

(c) Find the minimum number of sessions required for the monthly card to be the cheaper option.

Show all working.   **3**

[*END OF QUESTION PAPER*]

[BLANK PAGE]

C

2500/406

NATIONAL
QUALIFICATIONS
2006

FRIDAY, 5 MAY
2.45 PM – 4.05 PM

MATHEMATICS
STANDARD GRADE
Credit Level
Paper 2

1 **You may use a calculator**.

2 Answer as many questions as you can.

3 Full credit will be given only where the solution contains appropriate working.

4 Square-ruled paper is provided.

SCOTTISH
QUALIFICATIONS
AUTHORITY

FORMULAE LIST

The roots of $ax^2 + bx + c = 0$ are $x = \dfrac{-b \pm \sqrt{(b^2 - 4ac)}}{2a}$

Sine rule: $\dfrac{a}{\sin A} = \dfrac{b}{\sin B} = \dfrac{c}{\sin C}$

Cosine rule: $a^2 = b^2 + c^2 - 2bc \cos A$ or $\cos A = \dfrac{b^2 + c^2 - a^2}{2bc}$

Area of a triangle: Area $= \frac{1}{2}ab \sin C$

Standard deviation: $s = \sqrt{\dfrac{\sum(x - \bar{x})^2}{n-1}} = \sqrt{\dfrac{\sum x^2 - (\sum x)^2 / n}{n-1}}$, where n is the sample size.

KU | RE

1. The orbit of a planet around a star is circular.

The radius of the orbit is $4 \cdot 96 \times 10^7$ kilometres.

Calculate the circumference of the orbit.

Give your answer **in scientific notation**.

3

2. (a) The pulse rates, in beats per minute, of 6 adults in a hospital waiting area are:

68   73   86   72   82   78.

Calculate the mean and standard deviation of this data.

3

(b) 6 children in the same waiting area have a mean pulse rate of $89 \cdot 6$ beats per minute and a standard deviation of $5 \cdot 4$.

Make **two** valid comparisons between the children's pulse rates and those of the adults.

2

3. Harry bids successfully for a painting at an auction.

An "auction tax" of 8% is added to his bid price.

He pays £324 in total.

Calculate his bid price.

3

[Turn over

KU | RE

4. (*a*) Expand and simplify

$$(x+4)(3x-1).$$

1

(*b*) Expand

$$m^{\frac{1}{2}}(2+m^2).$$

2

(*c*) Simplify, leaving your answer as a surd

$$2\sqrt{20}-3\sqrt{5}.$$

2

5. ST, a vertical pole 2 metres high, is situated at the corner of a rectangular garden, PQRS.

RS is 8 metres long and QR is 12 metres long.

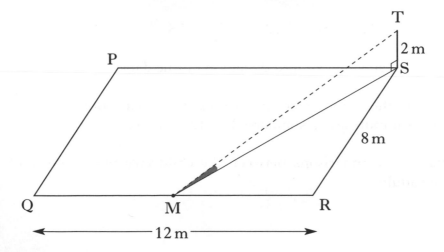

The pole casts a shadow over the garden.

The shadow reaches M, the midpoint of QR.

Calculate the size of the shaded angle TMS.

4

KU | RE

6. (a) There are three mooring points A, B and C on Lake Sorling.

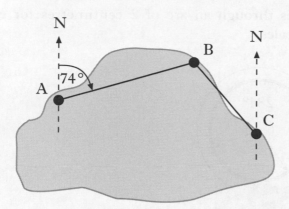

From A, the bearing of B is 074°.

From C, the bearing of B is 310°.

Calculate the size of angle ABC.

2

(b) B is 230 metres from A and 110 metres from C.

Calculate the direct distance from A to C.

Give your answer **to 3 significant figures**.

4

7. (a) A block of copper 18 centimetres long
is prism shaped as shown.

The area of its cross section is 28 square centimetres.

Find the volume of the block.

1

(b) The block is melted down to make a
cylindrical cable of diameter 14 **millimetres**.

Calculate the length of the cable.

4

KU | RE

8. A set of scales has a circular dial.

The pointer is 9 centimetres long.

The tip of the pointer moves through an arc of 2 centimetres for each 100 grams of weight on the scales.

A parcel, placed on the scales, moves the pointer through an angle of 284°.

Calculate the weight of the parcel.

4

9. The number of diagonals, *d*, in a polygon of *n* sides is given by the formula

$$d = \tfrac{1}{2} n (n - 3).$$

(a) How many diagonals does a polygon of 7 sides have?

2

(b) A polygon has 65 diagonals.

Show that for this polygon, $n^2 - 3n - 130 = 0$.

2

(c) Hence find the number of sides in this polygon.

3

KU | RE

10. Emma goes on the "Big Eye".

Her height, h metres, above the ground is given by the formula

$$h = -31 \cos t° + 33$$

where t is the number of seconds after the start.

(a) Calculate Emma's height above the ground 20 seconds after the start. 2

(b) When will Emma first reach a height of 60 metres above the ground? 3

(c) When will she next be at a height of 60 metres above the ground? 1

[Turn over for Question 11 on *Page eight*

11. In triangle ABC,

BC = 8 centimetres,

AC = 6 centimetres and

PQ is parallel to BC.

M is the midpoint of AC.

Q lies on AC, x centimetres from M, as shown on the diagram.

(a) Write down an expression for the length of AQ. **1**

(b) Show that PQ = $(4 + \frac{4}{3}x)$ centimetres. **3**

[END OF QUESTION PAPER]

[BLANK PAGE]

[BLANK PAGE]